Little Tom Tucker,
He sang for his supper.
What did he sing for?
Why, white bread and butter.
How can I cut it without a knife?
How can I marry without a wife?

First published in Great Britain in 1986
by Methuen Children's Books Ltd,
11 New Fetter Lane, London EC4P 4EE.

© Copyright 1986 Sheldrake Publishing Ltd

Designed and produced by Sheldrake Press Ltd
188 Cavendish Road, London SW12 0DA.

Designed by Ivor Claydon and Bob Hook

Illustrations researched and chosen
by Karin B. Hills, with grateful thanks to
the Colin Mears Collection

Typesetting by Rowland Phototypesetting (London) Ltd.

Printed and bound in England by W.S. Cowell Ltd., Butter Market, Ipswich.
ISBN 0 416 61510 4

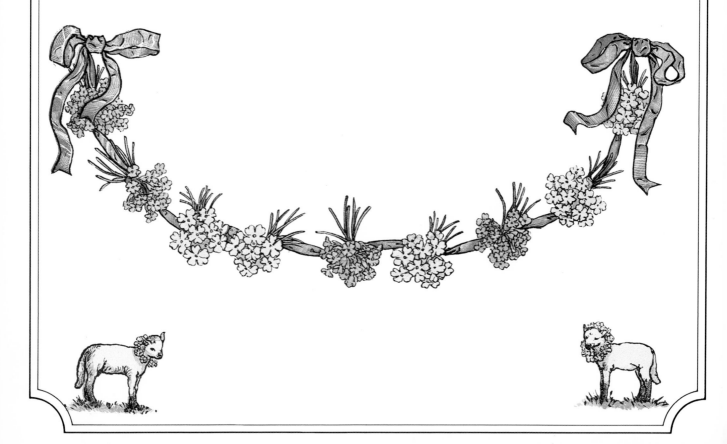

THE KATE GREENAWAY

BABY BOOK

METHUEN CHILDREN'S BOOKS

KATE GREENAWAY, the doyenne of nursery writers and illustrators, was born in London in 1846. Her father, John Greenaway, was a draughtsman and wood engraver working mainly for *The Illustrated London News*. Kate's greatest delight as a small girl was to creep downstairs while the rest of the family slept, to watch him labour through the night on an urgent engraving for the magazine. Recognizing that she had a passion for drawing, her parents sent her at the early age of 12 to the National Art Training School, now the Royal College of Art.

In 1868 she had a watercolour and six small drawings accepted for exhibition by the Dudley Gallery in Piccadilly, which in turn led to varied commissions for greetings cards, calendars, book and magazine illustrations. In 1877 came the turning point in her career, when she met the forward-thinking engraver and printer, Edmund Evans, and presented him with a collection of her own rhymes and pictures entitled *Under the Window*. Evans loved it at once, and had the conviction and courage to print a first edition of 20,000 copies. It sold out before he could reprint. For more than a decade thereafter the partnership flourished, producing such classics of children's literature as *Marigold Garden, Mother Goose, A Day in a Child's Life, A Apple Pie* and *Language of Flowers*.

Kate Greenaway died in 1901. Though she never had sons and daughters of her own, children remained her passion for life. 'No one has given us such clear-eyed, soft-faced, happy-hearted childhood,' wrote the poet Austin Dobson, 'or so poetically apprehended the coy reticences, the simplicities, and the small solemnities of little people'. With their charmingly adapted end-of-the-18th-century breeches, bonnets, smocks and frocks, the open-faced children in her illustrations reminded her readers of the true values of innocence, joy and beauty. They have lost none of their appeal or relevance today.

CONTENTS

THE BIRTH

Name_____ Time_____

Date_____ Place_____

Doctor————————————————— Name tag

Midwife/nurse—————————————

Newspaper announcement

Weight_____   Colour of hair_____

Length_____   Lock of hair

Colour of eyes_____

Resemblances _____ Personality _____

_____ _____

_____ _____

_____ _____

_____ _____

_____ _____

_____ _____

_____ _____

First visitors _____

_____

_____

_____

_____

_____

_____

_____

_____

_____

_____

_____

Gifts_____

_____

_____

_____

_____

_____

_____

_____

_____

_____

_____

_____

Cards_____

_____

_____

_____

_____

_____

_____

_____

_____

_____

_____

PHOTOGRAPHS

PHOTOGRAPHS

THE FAMILY TREE

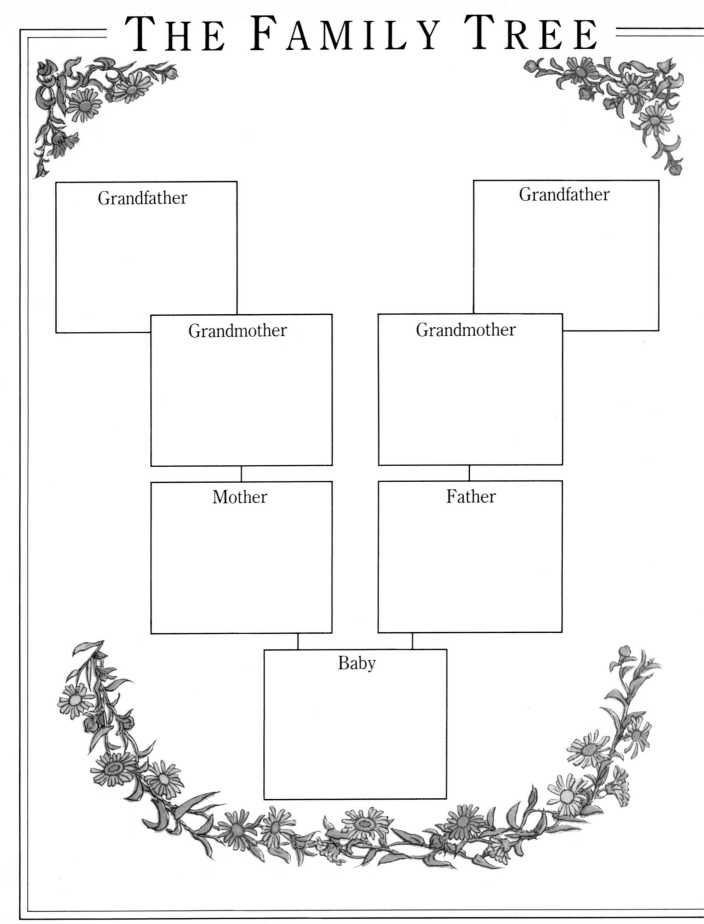

Grandfather

Grandfather

Grandmother

Grandmother

Mother

Father

Baby

Brothers and Sisters

_____

_____

_____

_____

_____

NAMING

Full name _____

_____

Date _____

Place _____

_____

Guests _____

_____

_____

_____

_____

_____

_____

_____

_____

Gifts _____

_____

_____

_____

_____

_____

_____

_____

_____

PHOTOGRAPHS

Weight _____ _____

Length _____ _____

General progress _____ _____

_____ _____

_____ _____

_____ _____

_____ _____

_____ _____

_____ _____

PHOTOGRAPHS

WEIGHT

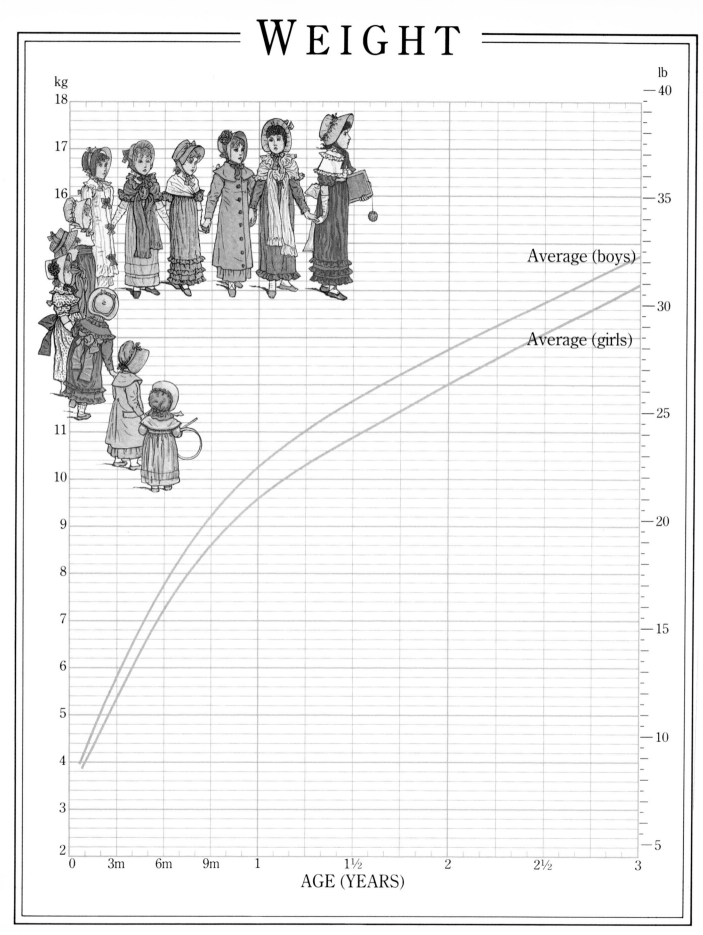

kg

lb

Average (boys)

Average (girls)

AGE (YEARS)

0   3m   6m   9m   1   1½   2   2½   3

HEIGHT

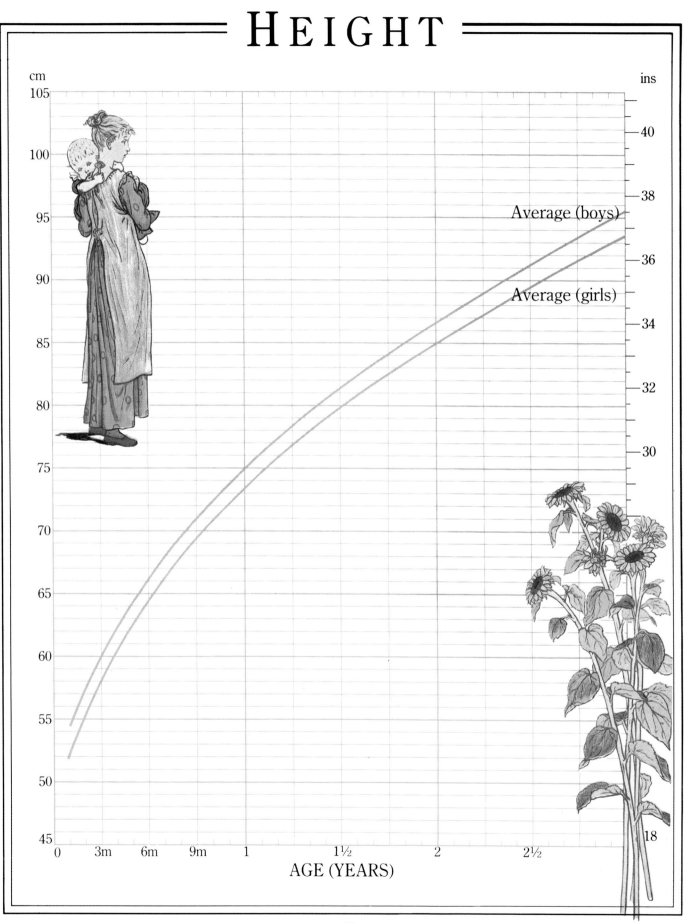

cm

105

100

95 — Average (boys)

90 — Average (girls)

85

80

75

70

65

60

55

50

45

ins

40

38

36

34

32

30

18

0   3m   6m   9m   1   1½   2   2½

AGE (YEARS)

VACCINATIONS

_____   _____

_____   _____

_____   _____

_____   _____

_____   _____

_____   _____
_____   _____
_____   _____
_____   _____
_____   _____
_____   _____
_____   _____
_____   _____
_____   _____
_____   _____

AT SIX MONTHS

Weight _____   _____

Length _____   _____

General progress _____   _____

_____   _____

_____   _____

_____   _____

_____   _____

_____   _____

_____   _____

_____   _____

PHOTOGRAPHS

TEETH

Date

UPPER JAW

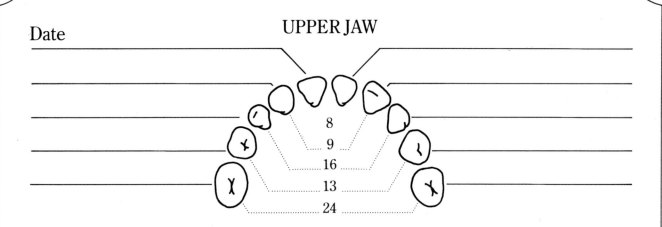

8
9
16
13
24

MONTHS

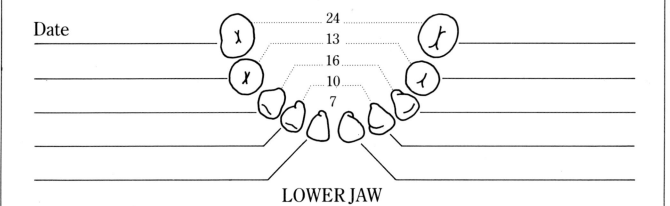

Date

24
13
16
10
7

LOWER JAW

FIRST WORDS

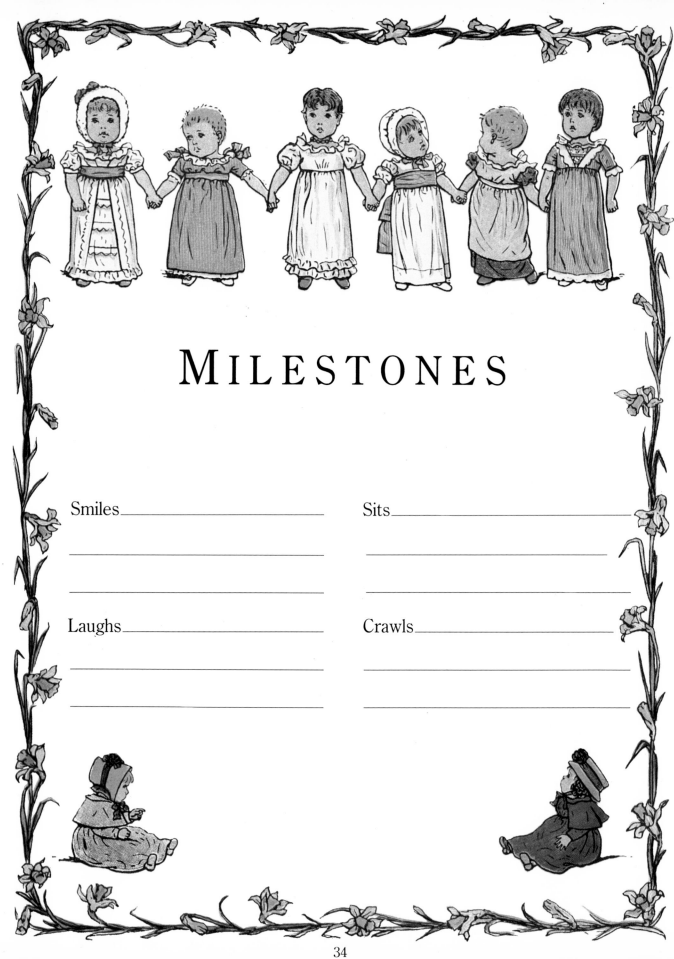

MILESTONES

Smiles_____

_____

_____

Sits_____

_____

_____

Laughs_____

_____

_____

Crawls_____

_____

_____

Stands

Walks

FIRST HOLIDAY

Spring.

Autumn.

Winter.

AT ONE YEAR

Weight_____

Height_____

General progress_____

_____

_____

_____

_____

_____

_____   _____

_____   _____

_____   _____

_____   _____

_____   _____

_____   _____

_____   _____

_____   _____

_____   _____

PHOTOGRAPHS

FIRST BIRTHDAY

Funny Sayings

AND INCIDENTS

_____   _____

_____   _____

_____   _____

_____   _____

_____   _____

_____   _____

_____   _____

_____   _____

_____   _____

FAVOURITES

Stories————————————————

————————————————————————

————————————————————————

————————————————————————

————————————————————————

————————————————————————

————————————————————————

————————————————————————

————————————————————————

Books————————————————

————————————————————————

————————————————————————

————————————————————————

Toys_____

Pets_____

_____

_____

_____

_____

_____

_____

_____

_____

_____

_____

_____

_____

_____

_____

Rhymes/poems_____   Games_____

_____   _____

_____   _____

_____   _____

_____   _____

_____   _____

_____   _____

_____   _____

Songs/lullabies_____

_____

_____

_____

Special interests_____

_____

_____

FIRST DRAWING

FIRST WRITING

GOING TO SCHOOL

Place _____

_____

Date _____

Teachers _____

_____

_____

_____

_____

Favourite activities _____

_____   _____

_____   _____

_____   _____

_____   _____

_____   _____

_____   _____

_____   _____

Special friends _____

_____

_____

_____

_____

_____

_____

Little Miss Muffet,
Sat on a tuffet,
Eating some curds and whey;
There came a great spider,
And sat down beside her,
And frightened Miss Muffet away.